Gold Stars®

Spelling

hutch

boy

blue

PaRragon

Bath · New York · Cologne · Melbourne · Delhi
Hong Kong · Shenzhen · Singapore

Helping your child

- The activities in this book will help your child to learn how to spell a variety of common words, including colours, numbers, days of the week and plurals.

- Children learn to spell by reading and writing. If your child finds a word difficult to spell, try to follow this method: LOOK at the word; COVER UP the word; WRITE the word; CHECK the word.

- It is important that you set aside time to do the activities together. Your child does not need to complete each page in one go. Do a little at a time and give lots of encouragement and praise.

- The answers to the activities are on page 32.

- Remember that the gold stars are a reward for effort as well as for achievement.

This edition published by Parragon Books Ltd in 2017

Parragon Books Ltd
Chartist House
15–17 Trim Street
Bath BA1 1HA, UK
www.parragon.com

Copyright © Parragon Books Ltd 2002–2017

Written by Betty Root and Nina Filipek
Illustrated by Simon Abbot
Educational Consultant: Martin Malcolm

ISBN 978-1-4748-7634-6

Printed in China

Contents

Choose one letter to make each word.

| a | b | c | d | e | f | g | h |

＿gg   ＿nt   ＿ap   ＿og

＿oat   ＿en   ＿ox   ＿ish

Copy the words in alphabetical order from a to h.

1. a _____   2. b _____

3. c _____   4. _____

5. _____   6. _____

7. _____   8. _____

Look at the pictures. Can you spot something that begins with each letter?

i	j	k	l	m	n	o	p	q	r

Fill in the gaps.

The __ing and __ueen had lots of pets.

They had a __ion, a __onkey and a __ig.

They had an __wl in a __est.

They had a __abbit with big ears.

They fed them all on __elly and __ce cream.

Put the words you made in alphabetical order, from i to r.

1. i _____

2. j _____

3. k _____

4. l _____

5. m _____

6. n _____

7. o _____

8. p _____

9. q _____

10. r _____

Note for parent: This activity focuses on alphabetical order. Remind your child that words are ordered alphabetically in dictionaries and other reference materials.

5

First letter sounds

Choose one letter to make each word.

| s | t | u | v | w | x | y | z |

_ap   _an   _asp   _ellow

_ip   _mbrella   _-ray   _un

Copy the words in alphabetical order from s to z.

1. s _____   **2.** t _____

3. u _____   **4.** v _____

5. w _____   **6.** _____

7. _____   **8.** _____

Note for parent: This activity focuses on alphabetical order. Remind your child that words are
ordered alphabetically in dictionaries and other reference materials.

Middle sounds

Write the missing letter to finish each word. Read the words.

    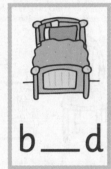

d__g   c__p   p__g   b__t   b__d

w__g   c__t   f__x   w__b   d__ck

n__t   s__n   r__t   b__s

First write **ch** to make each word. LOOK at the word. COVER it up. WRITE it on the line below. CHECK if you are right!

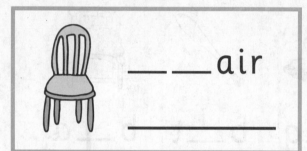

___air

_____

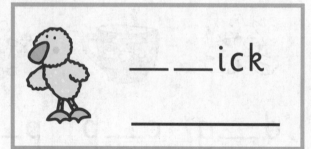

___ick

_____

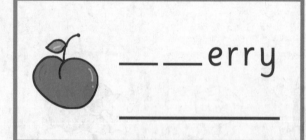

___erry

_____

___ildren

_____

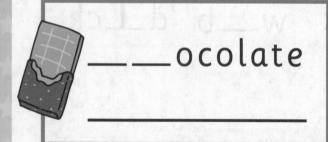

___ocolate

_____

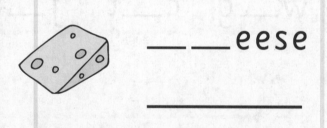

___eese

_____

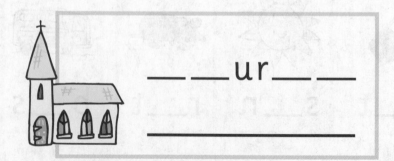

___ur___

_____

Note for parent: Remind your child to practise the LOOK, COVER, WRITE, CHECK method to spell other words in this book.

Wordsearch for **sh**

Look in the grid for words that begin or end with **sh**.
Circle them, then copy each word next to the right
picture.

s	h	a	r	k	n	b
h	m	f	o	d	e	r
e	d	i	s	h	s	u
e	h	s	r	u	l	s
p	s	h	e	d	o	h

Note for parent: Ask your child to try to spell these and other words containing the **sh** sound.
For example: shop, shell, dash, wish.

9

br sound

Write **br** in the gaps to make these words.
Read them out.

___ain	___anch
___oom	___idle
___ook	___ing
___im	___eeze
___onze	___ave

Draw a line to match each word to a picture.

bridge

brothers

brown

bricks

bread

Note for parent: Ask your child to try to spell these and other words containing the **br** sound. For example: bran, broth, brush, brisk.

Write **cr** in the gaps to make these words.
Read them out.

___ ___ y	___ ___ ash
___ ___ ew	___ ___ isp
___ ___ umb	___ ___ unch
___ ___ eak	___ ___ eam
___ ___ ate	___ ___ ust

Look at the picture clues. Write the
letters **cr** in the correct place in the
crossword.

Across	Down
🦀	👑
🖍️	🐊
✖️	

```
                        | a | b |
      | a | y | o | n |
                  | c |
  | o |       | o | s | s |
  | w |           | d |
  | n |           | i |
                  | l |
                  | e |
```

Note for parent: Ask your child to try to spell these and other words containing the **cr** sound.
For example: crop, crow, crack, crane.

11

Say the sounds:

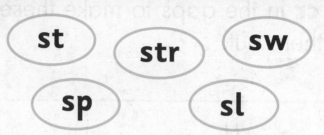

Say the name of each picture. Write the sound to match the picture.

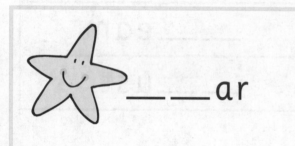 ___ar

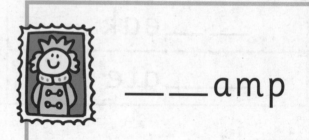 ___amp

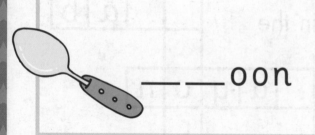 ___oon

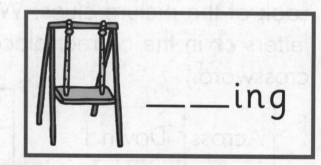 ___ing

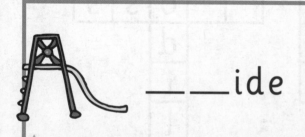 ___ide

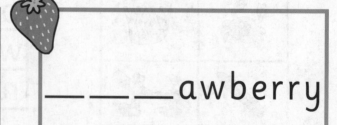 ___awberry

Note for parent: Ask your child to look in a dictionary for more words beginning with these sounds.

th sound

First write **th** to make each word. LOOK at the word. COVER it up. WRITE it on the line below. CHECK if you are right!

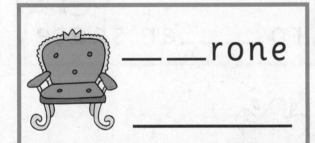 ___umb

_____

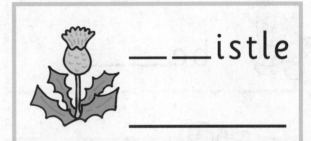 ___istle

_____

 ___rone

_____

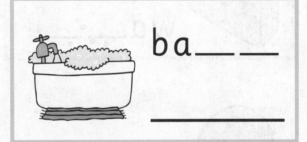 ba___

_____

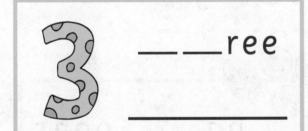 ___ree

_____

too___brush

_____

$3+2 = 5$
$9-6 = 3$

ma___s

_____

Note for parent: Ask your child to look in a dictionary for more words beginning with this sound.

13

Say the name of each picture. Spell the word next to each picture.

 be____

 umbre____a

 wa____

 ro____er skate

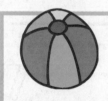 ba____

 ye____ow

 je____y

 ba____oons

caterpi____ars

Note for parent: Tell your child that in these words, double letters ll have a single vowel before them.

Double letters: oo

Say the name of each picture. Spell the word next to each picture.

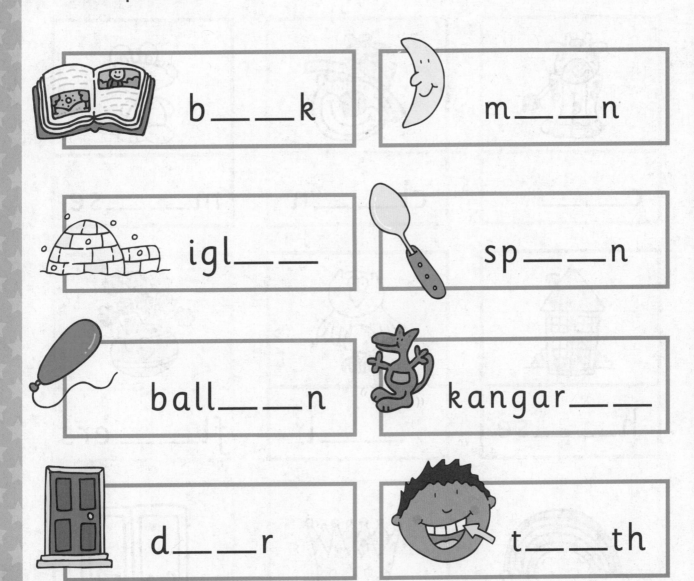

b _ _ k

m _ _ _ n

igl _ _ _

sp _ _ n

ball _ _ _ n

kangar _ _ _

d _ _ r

t _ _ _ th

h _ _ k

Note for parent: Tell your child that the double letters **oo** have different sounds in these words.

15

Say what is in the picture. Write **ow** or **ou** to finish off the word.

c____

cl____n

m____se

h____se

____l

fl____ers

rainb____

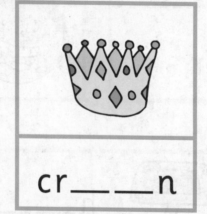

cr____n

wind____

Note to parent: Remind your child to listen for the different sounds of **ow** and **ou** in these words.

Middle sounds: **oa** and **ea**

Choose a word to fill each gap.

goat

pear

feather

coat

boat

1. I felt sea sick on the _____.

2. I saw a _____ on the farm.

3. I put on my _____.

4. I can eat a _____.

5. I found a _____.

Note for parent: This activity introduces common vowel combinations that are used to create different sounds.

17

Middle sound: ai

Say what is in the picture. Spell the word next to it.

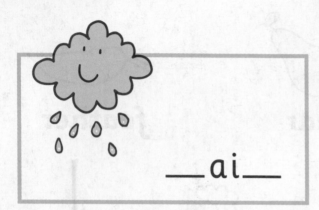

__ ai __

__ __ ai __

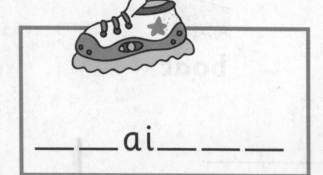

__ ai __ __ __

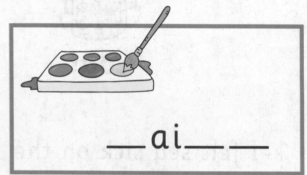

__ ai __ __

__ ai __

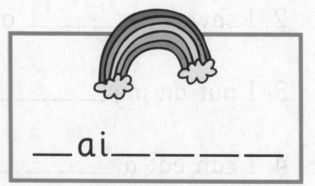

__ ai __ __ __ __

18

ee or ea?

Say what is in each picture.

Write each word on the correct list. Check your spellings in a dictionary.

ee	ea
cheese	

Note for parent: Tell your child that, in these words, the letters **ee** and **ea** sound the same.

19

Silent letters

Some words have silent letters. You see a silent letter in a word but you do not hear it when you say the word. Underline the letters that are silent in the words below.

knife   guitar   knight   wheel

comb   thumb   wrist   badge

gnome   knitting

Note for parent: Ask your child to try to spell these and other words containing silent letters.
For example: island, knee, limb, yacht.

Draw lines to join the words that end with the same sounds.

Choose words from this list to complete the rhyme.

out   sprout   spout   shout

rain   train   again

Incy Wincy Spider climbed up the water _____.

Down came the rain and washed the spider _____.

Out came the sunshine and dried up all the _____.

So Incy Wincy Spider climbed up the spout _____!

Note for parent: Ask your child to try to spell these rhyming words.

21

Everyday words

Copy the words from the box into the right sentences.

| laugh | because | here |
| once | water | would |

1. I _____ like a new bike.

2. I am staying indoors _____ it is raining.

3. My sister likes to make me _____ .

4. I _____ went to a football match.

5. I wash with _____ .

6. My house is _____ .

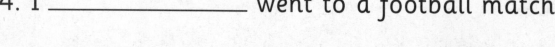

Note for parent: These common words are used frequently in the English language. It would be useful for your child to learn to spell them by heart.

LOOK at the word. COVER it up. WRITE it on the line. CHECK if you are right!

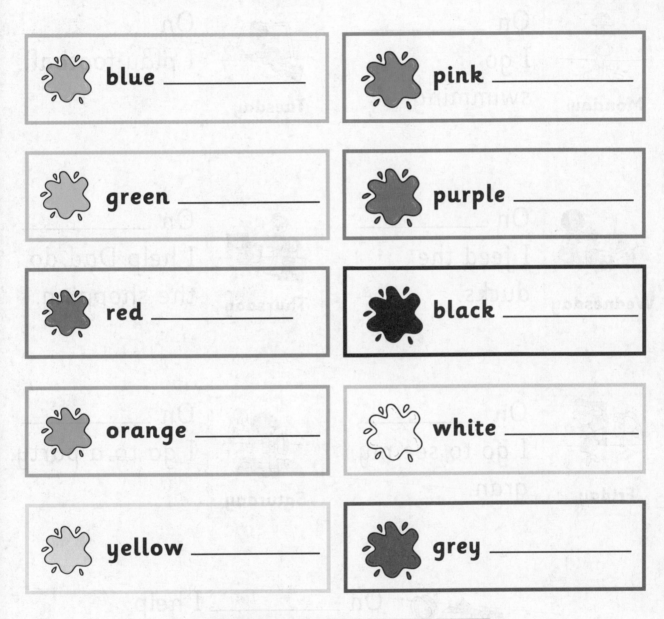

blue _____

pink _____

green _____

purple _____

red _____

black _____

orange _____

white _____

yellow _____

grey _____

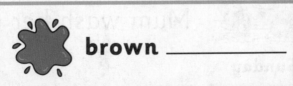

brown _____

Days of the week

Finish these sentences.

 **Monday** On _____ I go swimming.

 **Tuesday** On _____ I play football.

 **Wednesday** On _____ I feed the ducks.

 **Thursday** On _____ I help Dad do the shopping.

 **Friday** On _____ I go to see my gran.

 **Saturday** On _____ I go to a party.

 **Sunday** On _____ I help Mum wash her car.

Note for parent: Remind your child that the days of the week begin with a capital letter.

Compound words

A compound word is made up of two short ones.
Write a word by each picture. Join two pictures
to make a compound word.

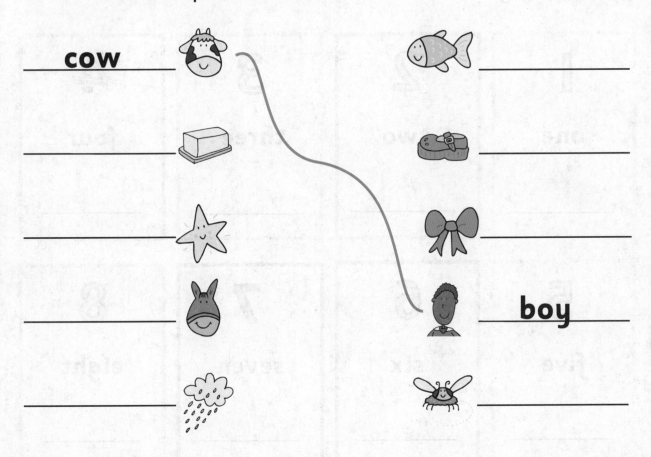

__**cow**__

__ __ __ __ __ __ __ __

__ __ __ __ __ __ __ __

__ __ __ __ __ __ __ __

__ __ __ __ __ __ __ __

__ __ __ __ __ __ __ __

__ __ __ __ __ __ __ __

__**boy**__

__ __ __ __ __ __ __ __

Now write your new words.

__**cowboy**__ __ __ __ __ __ __ __ __ __ __ __ __ __ __ __ __

__ __ __ __ __ __ __ __

Note for parent: Ask your child to try to spell these and other compound words.
For example: tugboat, hairbrush, dustbin, bedroom, notebook.

25

LOOK at the word. COVER UP the word with your finger. WRITE the word on the line below. CHECK if you are right!

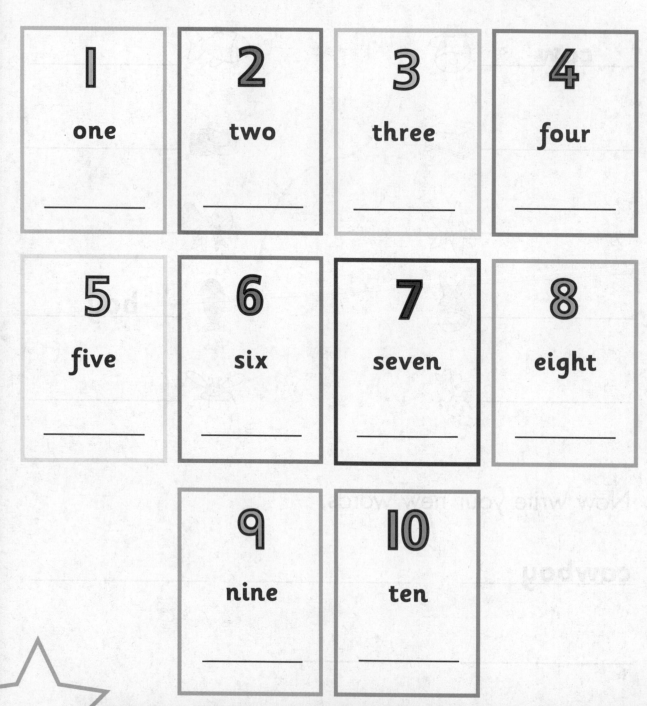

1 one	2 two	3 three	4 four
5 five	6 six	7 seven	8 eight
	9 nine	10 ten	

11 eleven ___	12 twelve ___	13 thirteen ___	14 fourteen ___
15 fifteen ___	16 sixteen ___	17 seventeen ___	18 eighteen ___
	19 nineteen ___	20 twenty ___	

Magic e

Add the letter **e** to a short word and magic happens. The vowel in the middle of the word changes its sound and the word changes its meaning.

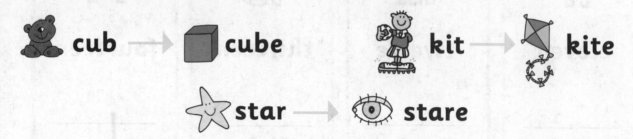

cub → cube   kit → kite

star → stare

Use magic **e** on these words.

cap → _ _ _ _   bit → _ _ _ _

hat → _ _ _ _   not → _ _ _ _

her → _ _ _ _   tub → _ _ _ _

The middles are missing from these words. Put the same missing letter in each pair of words, like this:

rid **and** ride

Choose from | a | e | i | o | u |

1. c__t **and** c__te   2. m__t **and** m__te

3. p__n **and** p__ne   4. h__p **and** h__pe

5. c__r **and** c__re   6. f__n **and** f__ne

More than one

Copy these words into the right boxes.

mouse	book	house
fox	cow	tooth
foxes	houses	cows
books	mice	teeth

One	More than one
mouse	mice
tooth	teeth

Note for parent: For most words we can add **-s**, **-es** or **-ies** to make the plural. But some words, such as 'mouse -> mice', change their spelling in more unusual ways.

29

Present and past

The present is something we are doing now. The past is something we have already done.

> **Present – I am painting a picture.**
>
> **Past – I have painted a picture.**

Add <u>ing</u> for the present and <u>ed</u> for the past.

Present	Past
wait_____	wait___
jump_____	jump___
sail_____	sail___
walk_____	walk___
talk_____	talk___

Present	Past
crawl_____	crawl___
climb_____	climb___
wash_____	wash___
brush_____	brush___
laugh_____	laugh___
cook_____	cook___

Note for parent: This activity introduces the present and past tenses.

Tricky words

Some words are tricky to spell because they don't follow normal spelling patterns. Here are some of them.

 **anchor**

 **pyjamas**

 **biscuit**

 whistle

 **chef**

 **penguin**

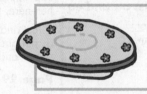 **saucer**

Copy out any of these words you find hard to spell. Cover them up, then write them from memory. Keep going until you know the spelling.

_____   _____

_____   _____

_____   _____

_____   _____

Note for parent: Ask your child to use the LOOK, COVER, WRITE, CHECK method to learn to spell these words.

31

Answers

Pages 4-5 First letter sounds

egg ant cap dog goat hen box fish

1. ant 2. box 3. cap 4. dog
5. egg 6. fish 7. goat 8. hen

The king and queen had lots of pets.

They had a lion, a monkey and a pig.

They had an owl in a nest.

They had a rabbit with big ears.

They fed them all on jelly and ice cream.

1. ice cream 2. jelly 3. king 4. lion
5. monkey 6. nest 7. owl 8. pig
9. queen 10. rabbit

Page 6 First letter sounds

tap van wasp yellow zip umbrella
x-ray sun

1. sun 2. tap 3. umbrella 4. van
5. wasp 6. x-ray 7. yellow 8. zip

Page 7 Middle sounds

dog, cup, pig, bat, bed, wig, cat, fox,
web, duck, net, sun, rat, bus

Page 8 ch sound

chair, chick, cherry, children, chocolate,
cheese, church

Page 9 Wordsearch for sh

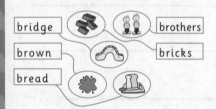

shark, brush, shed, sheep, dish, fish

Page 10 br sound

brain, branch, broom, bridle, brook,
bring, brim, breeze, bronze, brave

bridge
brown
bread

brothers
bricks

Page 11 cr sound

cry, crash,
crew, crisp,
crumb, crunch,
creak, cream,
crate, crust

crab
crayon
crocodile
crown
cross

Page 12 Sounds: st, str, sp, sl, sw

star, stamp, spoon, swing, slide,
strawberry

Page 13 th sound

thumb, thistle, throne, bath, three,
toothbrush, maths

Page 14 Double letters: ll

bell, umbrella, wall, roller skate, ball,
yellow, jelly, balloons, caterpillars

Page 15 Double letters: oo

book, moon, igloo, spoon, balloon,
kangaroo, door, tooth, hook

Page 16 ow or ou?

cow, clown, mouse, house, owl, flowers,
rainbow, crown, window

Page 17 Middle sounds: oa and ea

1. I felt sea sick on the boat.
2. I saw a goat on the farm.
3. I put on my coat.
4. I can eat a pear.
5. I found a feather.

Page 18 Middle sound: ai

rain, train, trainer, paint, hair, rainbow

Page 19 ee or ea?

ee	ea
cheese	ice cream
queen	leaf
wheel	
tree	

Page 20 Silent letters

knife, guitar, knight, wheel, comb, thumb,
wrist, badge, gnome, knitting

Page 21 Rhyming words

Incy Wincy Spider climbed up the water
spout.

Down came the rain and washed the
spider out.

Out came the sunshine and dried up all
the rain.

So Incy Wincy Spider climbed up the
spout again.

Page 22 Everyday words

1. would 2. because 3. laugh
4. once 5. water 6. here

Page 24 Days of the week

On Monday I go swimming.

On Tuesday I play football.

On Wednesday I feed the ducks.

On Thursday I help Dad do the shopping.

On Friday I go to see my gran.

On Saturday I go to a party.

On Sunday I help Mum wash her car.

Page 25 Compound words

cow+boy = cowboy, butter+fly = butterfly,
star+fish = starfish, horse+shoe =
horseshoe, rain+bow = rainbow

Page 28 Magic e

cap–cape, bit–bite, hat–hate, not–note,
her–here, tub–tube

1. cut and cute   2. mat and mate
3. pin and pine 4. hop and hope
5. car and care 6. fin and fine

Page 29 More than one

One: mouse, book, house, fox, cow, tooth

More than one: mice, books, houses,
foxes, cows, teeth

Page 30 Present and past

Present	Past
waiting	waited
jumping	jumped
sailing	sailed
walking	walked
talking	talked
crawling	crawled
climbing	climbed
washing	washed
brushing	brushed
laughing	laughed
cooking	cooked